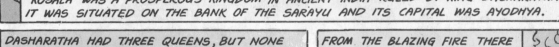

*A SWEET DISH MADE OF MILK AND RICE

1

THE KING TOOK THE PRECIOUS GIFT FIRST TO KAUSALYA, HIS ELDEST QUEEN.

KAUSALYA, PLEASE HAVE HALF OF THIS. YOU WILL HAVE A SON.

HE SHARED THE REMAINING BETWEEN HIS OTHER TWO WIVES, SUMITRA AND KAIKEYI. IN DUE COURSE, FOUR SONS WERE BORN. KAUSALYA'S SON WAS NAMED RAMA AND KAIKEYI'S SON WAS NAMED BHARATA. SUMITRA HAD TWINS, LAKSHMANA AND SHATRUGHNA.

THE PRINCES LEARNT THE VEDAS.

THEY LEARNT HOW TO RIDE HORSES AND ELEPHANTS.

BEFORE THEY WERE SIXTEEN, THEY HAD MASTERED THE USE OF WEAPONS.

ONE DAY, AS DASHARATHA SAT AT COURT WITH HIS MINISTERS, A ROYAL GUARD ENTERED THE HALL.

YOUR MAJESTY! SAGE VISHWAMITRA HAS COME TO SEE YOU.

THE KING HURRIED OUT TO RECEIVE THE SAGE.

AFTER THE SAGE HAD COME IN AND ACCEPTED A SEAT, THE KING ADDRESSED HIM —

HOLY ONE! TELL ME THE PURPOSE OF YOUR VISIT. IS THERE ANYTHING YOU DESIRE? I'LL CARRY OUT YOUR ORDERS WITHOUT QUESTION.

THE RAKSHASAS* OBSTRUCT MY FIRE SACRIFICES. AS EACH SACRIFICE NEARS COMPLETION, THEY DEFILE THE ALTAR.

SEND YOUR VALIANT SON, RAMA, WITH ME TO DESTROY THEM.

OH, NO!

3

* DEMONS

DASHARATHA WAS SHOCKED BY THE WORDS OF THE SAGE AND, LOSING CONSCIOUSNESS, HE FELL DOWN.

WHEN HE RECOVERED —

RAMA IS NOT YET SIXTEEN. HE HAS NO EXPERIENCE OF WAR. HOW CAN HE FIGHT THE MIGHTY RAKSHASAS?

TAKE MY ARMY. IF YOU WISH, I'LL COME MYSELF TO FIGHT THE RAKSHASAS. BUT SPARE MY DARLING SON, RAMA.

IT HAS TO BE RAMA — AND NO ONE ELSE.

O KING, YOU HAVE GONE BACK ON YOUR WORD. THIS ILL BEFITS THE NOBLE TRADITION OF YOUR FAMILY. I TAKE MY LEAVE OF YOU, O UNTRUTHFUL KING!

THEN VASISHTHA, THE ROYAL PRECEPTOR, INTERVENED.

WAIT, VISHWAMITRA!

NO ONE LEAVES KING DASHARATHA'S COURT DISSATISFIED.

HE TURNED TO THE KING.

YOUR SON WILL COME TO NO HARM IN THE PROTECTION OF VISHWAMITRA WHO IS QUITE CAPABLE OF DESTROYING THE RAKSHASAS HIMSELF.

IT IS FOR RAMA'S OWN GOOD — TO TRAIN HIM IN WARFARE — THAT VISHWAMITRA HAS CHOSEN TO TAKE HIM. O KING, BE TRUE TO YOUR WORD AND LET RAMA GO.

DASHARATHA ACCEPTED THE ADVICE AND SENT FOR RAMA AND LAKSHMANA.

CHILDREN, GO WITH SAGE VISHWAMITRA AND CARRY OUT HIS COMMANDS.

THE THREE LEFT AYODHYA, CROSSED THE CONFLUENCE OF THE SARAYU AND THE GANGA, AND PROCEEDED FURTHER.

O RAMA, ONCE THIS PLACE WAS ALIVE WITH PEOPLE. THE WICKED RAKSHASI*, TATAKA, HAS DEVASTATED IT. SAVE THIS LAND BY DESTROYING HER.

AS YOU COMMAND, SIR.

AS RAMA LIFTED HIS BOW, THE SOUND OF ITS STRING ECHOED THROUGH THE FOREST. TATAKA HEARD THE SOUND—

TWANG

A TRESPASSER! I'LL DEVOUR HIM.

RUNNING TOWARDS HIM, SHE THREW A SHOWER OF ROCKS WHICH RAMA PARRIED WITH EASE.

SHE MADE HERSELF INVISIBLE AND CONTINUED TO SHOWER HEAVY ROCKS ON THEM.

SLAY HER!

BUT WHERE IS SHE?

THERE!

RAMA SENT A SHOWER OF ARROWS IN HER DIRECTION.

BUT TATAKA CONTINUED TO ADVANCE MENACINGLY.

GRRRR

THEN RAMA'S ARROW PIERCED HER HEART...

...AND SHE FELL DEAD.

VISHWAMITRA WAS PLEASED WITH RAMA'S VALOUR, SO HE PROCEEDED TO REVEAL THE SECRETS OF THE DIVINE WEAPONS TO HIM.

THEY RESUMED THEIR JOURNEY AND SOON ARRIVED AT THE SAGE'S HERMITAGE. THE ASCETICS RECEIVED THEM.

O GREAT SAGE, BEGIN YOUR SACRIFICE WITHOUT DELAY AND MAY SUCCESS ATTEND UPON YOU!

RAMA AND LAKSHMANA KEPT VIGIL AS THE SACRIFICE PROGRESSED. ON THE SIXTH DAY—

LOOK, LAKSHMANA! THE RAKSHASAS!

JUST AS THE WIND SCATTERS THE CLOUDS SO SHALL WE DESTROY THEM!

RAMA'S ARROW FOUND ITS MARK. THE RAKSHASA, MARICHA, WAS HIT WITH SUCH FORCE...

...THAT HE WAS FLUNG INTO THE SEA, A HUNDRED MILES AWAY.

SUBAHU AND THE OTHER RAKSHASAS WERE ALSO VANQUISHED BY RAMA AND LAKSHMANA. MEANWHILE THE FIRE SACRIFICE WAS COMPLETED SUCCESSFULLY.

I ONLY DID MY DUTY, HOLY ONE.

I'VE ACCOMPLISHED MY MISSION BECAUSE YOU CARRIED OUT MY WISHES. O RAMA, YOU'VE MADE MY SIDDHA-ASHRAM* WORTHY OF ITS NAME.

* THE HERMITAGE WHERE THE TASKS UNDERTAKEN ARE SUCCESSFULLY ACCOMPLISHED

THEN THE SAGES WHO HAD ATTENDED VISHWAMITRA'S SACRIFICE SPOKE TO RAMA.

PRINCE, WE ARE GOING TO MITHILA TO ATTEND THE YAGNA TO BE PERFORMED BY KING JANAKA. WHY DON'T YOU COME WITH US?

GLADLY!

SO RAMA AND LAKSHMANA SET OFF WITH VISHWAMITRA AND THE OTHER SAGES. ON THE WAY THE SAGES TOLD RAMA ABOUT SHIVA'S FAMOUS BOW WHICH WAS NOW IN THE POSSESSION OF JANAKA.

COULD WE SEE SHIVA'S BOW WHEN WE ARRIVE AT MITHILA?

YOU COULD, IF KING JANAKA GIVES HIS PERMISSION.

AT MITHILA, WHEN KING JANAKA CALLED ON VISHWAMITRA AND THE OTHER SAGES TO PAY HIS RESPECTS AND TO INVITE THEM TO THE SACRIFICE, HE NOTICED RAMA AND HIS BROTHER.

HOLY ONE, WHO ARE THESE TWO PRINCES WHO SHINE LIKE THE SUN AND THE MOON?

THEY ARE THE SONS OF DASHARATHA.

THE NEXT DAY, VISHWAMITRA AND THE PRINCES CALLED ON JANAKA AT THE SACRIFICIAL SITE.

O KING, THE PRINCES ARE EAGER TO SEE THE GREAT BOW.

MANY KINGS, O SAGE, HAVE TRIED IN VAIN TO STRING THE GREAT BOW OF SHIVA. IF RAMA SUCCEEDS IN THIS, HE SHALL MARRY MY DAUGHTER, SITA.

SITA WAS JANAKA'S ADOPTED DAUGHTER. WHILE PLOUGHING A SACRIFICIAL SITE HE HAD FOUND HER IN ONE OF THE FURROWS.

SOON, AT JANAKA'S COMMAND, FIVE HUNDRED STRONG MEN BROUGHT FROM THE CITY THE EIGHT-WHEELED BOX IN WHICH THE GREAT BOW WAS KEPT.

O SAGE, HERE IS THE GREAT BOW OF SHIVA. THE PRINCES MAY EXAMINE IT.

RAMA OPENED THE BOX AND LIFTED UP THE BOW EFFORTLESSLY.

EVEN AS HE STRUNG IT...

...THE BOW BROKE INTO TWO WITH A THUNDEROUS SOUND THAT SHOOK THE EARTH.

WHEN HE HAD RECOVERED FROM THE SHOCK, JANAKA TURNED TO VISHWAMITRA.

I AM INDEED FORTUNATE TO HAVE WITNESSED SUCH A FEAT. MY DAUGHTER SHALL HAVE RAMA AS HER LORD, AND ENHANCE THE GLORY OF MY DYNASTY. WITH YOUR PERMISSION I WILL CONVEY THE GLAD NEWS TO KING DASHARATHA.

IN DUE COURSE, DASHARATHA ARRIVED IN MITHILA TO ATTEND THE MARRIAGE CEREMONY.

O RAMA, FROM THIS MOMENT, MY DAUGHTER, THE VIRTUOUS SITA, WILL BE YOUR COMPANION! SHE WILL FOLLOW YOU LIKE A SHADOW. MAY YOU BOTH BE HAPPY!

LAKSHMANA MARRIED SITA'S SISTER, URMILA. BHARATA MARRIED MANDAVI AND SHATRUGHNA MARRIED SHRUTAKIRTI, BOTH DAUGHTERS OF JANAKA'S BROTHER, KING KUSHADHWAJA. FLOWERS RAINED DOWN FROM HEAVEN AS THEY WENT ROUND THE SACRED FIRE.

AFTER THE CEREMONY, VISHWAMITRA BLESSED THE PRINCES AND THEIR BRIDES...

...AND LEFT FOR THE HIMALAYAS TO MEDITATE.

DASHARATHA SET OUT FOR HIS CAPITAL WITH HIS SONS AND THEIR BRIDES. ON THE WAY, SAGE PARASHURAMA, A SWORN ENEMY OF THE WARRIOR CLASS, BARRED THE WAY.

O RAMA, HAVING HEARD ABOUT YOUR HEROIC ACHIEVEMENTS, I'VE COME TO SEEK COMBAT WITH YOU!

DASHARATHA TREMBLED ALL OVER.

O HOLY ONE! SPARE MY SON WHO IS BUT A CHILD, I IMPLORE YOU!

IGNORING DASHARATHA'S PLEAS, PARASHURAMA BROUGHT FORTH HIS BOW.

HERE, TAKE THIS GREAT BOW OF VISHNU. IF YOU SUCCEED IN DRAWING THIS BOW, I'LL CONSIDER YOU WORTHY OF MY RESPECT!

RAMA THEN SEIZED THE BOW, AND PLACED AN ARROW IN IT, READY FOR USE.

O, RAMA, I AM NOW CONVINCED THAT YOU ARE NONE OTHER THAN VISHNU!

PARSHURAMA RETURNED TO HIS ABODE IN MOUNT MAHENDRA AND DASHARATHA RESUMED HIS JOURNEY WITH HIS PARTY.

AYODHYA GAVE A ROUSING WELCOME TO THE PRINCES AND THEIR BRIDES.

SOME TIME LATER, BHARATA WENT TO HIS MATERNAL GRANDFATHER'S KINGDOM ON A VISIT.

RAMA TOOK GOOD CARE OF HIS FATHER.

HE IS AFFECTIONATE AND CONSIDERATE.

TWELVE YEARS PASSED BY.

I AM GETTING OLD. RAMA IS LOVED BY ALL. IT IS TIME TO NAME HIM MY SUCCESSOR.

DASHARATHA CALLED A MEETING OF HIS COUNCIL.

I HAVE RULED THIS GREAT KINGDOM IN ACCORDANCE WITH THE TRADITIONS OF MY ANCESTORS. NOW I HAVE GROWN OLD AND···

...WITH YOUR CONSENT, I DESIRE TO INSTALL MY ELDEST SON, RAMA, BEST AMONG MEN, AS YUVARAJA*.

WE APPROVE!

RAMA IS THE PERFECT CHOICE!

YES! IN FORBEARANCE, RAMA IS LIKE THE EARTH; IN WISDOM LIKE BRIHASPATI; IN VALOUR LIKE INDRA!

THEN DASHARATHA SENT FOR RAMA.

MY SON, ACCEPT THE HIGH OFFICE OF YUVARAJA. RULE YOUR SUBJECTS WITH DUE REGARD FOR THEIR HAPPINESS.

THANK YOU, FATHER.

* CROWN PRINCE

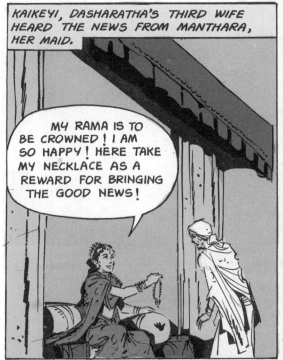

KAIKEYI, DASHARATHA'S THIRD WIFE HEARD THE NEWS FROM MANTHARA, HER MAID.

MY RAMA IS TO BE CROWNED! I AM SO HAPPY! HERE TAKE MY NECKLACE AS A REWARD FOR BRINGING THE GOOD NEWS!

BUT MANTHARA FLUNG THE NECKLACE AWAY.

THIS IS NO JOYOUS OCCASION! RAMA WILL BE KING AND BHARATA — NOTHING!

BUT, MANTHARA, RAMA IS AS DEAR TO ME AS BHARATA.

O FOOLISH QUEEN, CAN'T YOU SEE WHY THEY HAVE DECIDED TO CROWN RAMA IN BHARATA'S ABSENCE?

WHEN RAMA BECOMES KING, HE WILL EITHER BANISH BHARATA OR PUT HIM TO DEATH!

NO, HE WON'T. I KNOW MY RAMA!

BUT MANTHARA CONTINUED RELENTLESSLY—

KAUSALYA WILL BECOME THE QUEEN-MOTHER AND YOU'LL HAVE TO BOW TO HER WISHES!

MANTHARA'S WORDS HAD THE DESIRED EFFECT, FOR KAIKEYI WAS JEALOUS OF KAUSALYA.

PERHAPS YOU ARE RIGHT....

FOR YOUR SON'S SAKE — AND YOUR OWN — YOU MUST THINK OF A WAY TO GET RID OF RAMA.

PERSUADE THE KING TO PLACE BHARATA ON THE THRONE INSTEAD!

BUT HOW? WILL THE KING LISTEN TO ME?

HAVE YOU FORGOTTEN THE BOONS THE KING BESTOWED ON YOU?

YES! I COULD USE THEM NOW.

THE NEXT MORNING, THE NOBLES ASSEMBLED IN THE ROYAL COURT TO WITNESS THE INVESTITURE OF RAMA AS CROWN-PRINCE.

PREPARATIONS FOR THE CEREMONY ARE NOW COMPLETE. BUT WHERE IS THE KING?

I HOPE THERE IS NOTHING WRONG.

HONOURABLE SUMANTRA, WE HAVE BEEN WAITING FOR THE KING. WHY THE DELAY?

I AM SORRY I CAN'T STOP TO EXPLAIN JUST NOW. I AM ON MY WAY TO RAMA'S PALACE.

WHEN SUMANTRA REACHED RAMA'S PALACE —

PRINCE, THE KING WISHES TO SEE YOU. HE IS IN THE APARTMENTS OF QUEEN KAIKEYI.

I WILL GO RIGHT AWAY.

THEN RAMA TURNED TO SITA.

SITA, MOTHER KAIKEYI IS KIND AND CONSIDERATE: SHE IS PROBABLY DISCUSSING THE DETAILS OF THE CEREMONY WITH MY FATHER. I MUST HASTEN TO MEET THEM.

RAMA DROVE OUT TO KAIKEYI'S PALACE, PAST THE STREETS OF AYODHYA WHICH WERE GAILY DECORATED TO CELEBRATE HIS CORONATION. THE PEOPLE CHEERED HIM LUSTILY AS HE DROVE BY.

WHEN RAMA ENTERED KAIKEYI'S PALACE —

MY FATHER SEEMS TO BE IN GREAT DISTRESS. WHY IS HE NOT HAPPY TO SEE ME? WHY IS HE FROWNING?

HE TURNED TO KAIKEYI —

HAVE I OFFENDED MY FATHER? PLEASE PLEAD ON MY BEHALF, O MOTHER, AND ASK HIM TO FORGIVE ME.

O RAMA; IF YOU ONLY KNEW KAIKEYI'S TRUE NATURE!

RAMA, LONG AGO YOUR FATHER HAD PROMISED ME TWO BOONS. HE IS SILENT AND RESENTFUL BECAUSE THE FULFILMENT OF THOSE BOONS WILL CAUSE YOU UNPLEASANTNESS.

I AM PREPARED TO THROW MYSELF INTO FIRE IF MY FATHER DESIRES IT. PLEASE LET ME KNOW THE BOONS AND I PROMISE TO FULFIL THEM.

"HE FOUGHT BRAVELY AND KILLED MANY ASURAS."

O, RAMA, LONG AGO I HAD ACCOMPANIED THE KING WHEN HE SET OUT TO FIGHT THE ASURAS.

"IN THE COURSE OF THE BATTLE AN ARROW HIT HIM AND HE FELL WOUNDED. SENSING THE DANGER TO HIS LIFE, I DROVE THE CHARIOT THROUGH THE BESIEGING ARMY OF THE ASURAS...

"...AND BROUGHT HIM BACK SAFELY TO THE CAPITAL. THEN — "

KAIKEYI, I OWE MY LIFE TO YOU. ASK FOR TWO BOONS.

LORD, I SHALL CLAIM THEM WHEN THE NEED ARISES.

KAIKEYI CONCLUDED HER STORY —

AND THE NEED HAS ARISEN NOW. IF YOU AND YOUR FATHER WOULD UPHOLD THE TRUTH THEN YOU WILL LISTEN TO ME.

I WANT BHARATA TO BE MADE THE YUVARAJA AND YOU, RAMA, EXILED TO THE FOREST FOR FOURTEEN YEARS.

AT THESE WORDS, DASHA-RATHA WAS AGAIN OVERWHELMED WITH GRIEF.

O, RAMA!

BUT RAMA BETRAYED NO SIGN OF DISTRESS.

TO FULFIL THE PROMISE MADE BY THE KING, MY FATHER, I SHALL LEAVE FOR THE FOREST IMMEDIATELY.

MY RAMA!

BUT WHY DOESN'T MY FATHER TALK TO ME AFFECTIONATELY? I FEEL DISTRESSED TO SEE HIM SHEDDING TEARS.

IT IS BECAUSE HE CANNOT BRING HIMSELF TO ASK YOU TO GO TO THE FOREST. BUT HE WILL NEITHER BATHE NOR PARTAKE OF FOOD UNTIL YOU LEAVE.

ON HEARING THE WORDS OF KAIKEYI, DASHARATHA GOT UP —

FIE UPON YOU, O KAI....

FATHER!

20

OVERCOME BY SORROW, HE FELL DOWN UNCONSCIOUS.

O, FATHER!

THEN RAMA TURNED TO KAIKEYI—

MOTHER, YOU COULD HAVE ASKED ME TO GO TO THE FOREST WITHOUT CLAIMING THE PROMISED BOONS AND CAUSING DISTRESS TO MY FATHER. I WOULD HAVE GLADLY OBEYED YOU.

ON HIS WAY OUT, WHILE PASSING THROUGH THE PALACE HALL, RAMA WALKED ROUND THE SACRED ARTICLES ARRANGED FOR THE CORONATION AND PRAYED.

MAY THESE BE DEDICATED TO THE CORONATION OF BHARATA! MAY THE GODS PROTECT HIM!

BY THEN THE NOBLES WHO HAD ASSEMBLED IN THE PALACE HALL TO WITNESS THE CORONATION HAD LEARNT OF KAIKEYI'S DEMAND AND RAMA'S DECISION.

HE DOESN'T SEEM TO BE SORRY TO GIVE UP THE THRONE!

THERE HE GOES LIKE A YOGI!

RAMA CALLED ON KAUSALYA, HIS MOTHER, TO BID HER GOODBYE —

O CHILD, HOW CAN I BEAR THIS? TO HAVE A SON AND THEN TO BE SEPARATED FROM HIM IS WORSE THAN HAVING NO CHILD AT ALL!

WHEN LAKSHMANA SAW KAUSALYA IN TEARS, HE WAS OVERCOME WITH GRIEF.

OUR FATHER HAS LOST HIS SENSES IN HIS OLD AGE OR HE WOULD NOT HAVE DEPRIVED SINLESS RAMA OF THE KINGDOM AND EXILED HIM!

HE TURNED TO RAMA —

THE KING CANNOT CONFER THE KINGDOM ON BHARATA, IGNORING YOUR RIGHTS AS HIS ELDEST SON.

THE MEEK ARE EVER OPPRESSED. ASSERT YOURSELF. IF ANY ONE DARES OPPOSE YOU, I WILL DEAL WITH HIM.

LAKSHMANA, IN SUCH CIRCUMSTANCES, A MAN SHOULD STRIVE TO UPHOLD HIS DHARMA*. GIVE UP THIS RELIANCE ON VIOLENCE. I WILL BE ACTING AGAINST MY DHARMA IF I PREVENT THE FULFILMENT OF MY FATHER'S PROMISES.

IF YOU CANNOT CHANGE YOUR MIND, LET ME, TOO, GO WITH YOU INTO EXILE.

* DIVINE LAW, OBSERVANCE OF WHICH IS CONSIDERED A DUTY

MOTHER, THE KING IS ALREADY DEEPLY DISTRESSED. HE WILL DIE IF YOU DESERT HIM. YOUR PLACE IS BESIDE HIM. GIVE ME YOUR BLESSING AND LET ME GO.

KAUSALYA REALISED THAT IT WAS FUTILE TO TRY AND STOP HIM. SHE GAVE HER BLESSING AND THREW RICE OVER HIS HEAD.

GO, MY SON!

SHE THEN APPLIED SANDALWOOD PASTE ON HIS FOREHEAD.

MAY THE GODS OF THE MOUNTAINS, SEAS, RIVERS, SPACE, DAY AND NIGHT AND THE STARS PROTECT YOU IN THE FOREST.

THEN RAMA WENT TO SITA TO TAKE HIS LEAVE OF HER.

O RAMA, I WON'T BE SEPARATED FROM YOU! I SHALL ACCOMPANY YOU TO THE FOREST!

SITA, THE FOREST IS FULL OF BEASTS. IT IS NO PLACE FOR A DELICATE LADY. YOU ARE USED TO COMFORTS. STAY HERE IN THE PALACE.

MY LORD, IN YOUR COMPANY THE FOREST WILL BE LIKE HEAVEN AND WITHOUT YOU EVEN THE PALACE WILL BE HELL. TAKE ME WITH YOU! DON'T ABANDON ME!

NOW THAT I KNOW YOUR MIND, I SHALL TAKE YOU WITH ME.

THEN LAKSHMANA TURNED TO RAMA.

I WILL COME, TOO, RAMA! WITHOUT YOU I DESIRE NOTHING, NOT EVEN IMMORTALITY. TAKE ME WITH YOU!

VERY WELL, BROTHER. YOU SHALL BE A SOLACE TO ME.

RAMA GAVE AWAY HIS WEALTH ...

...AND SET OUT FOR DASHARATHA'S PALACE ON FOOT. THE PEOPLE WATCHED THEIR BELOVED PRINCE WITH TEARS IN THEIR EYES.

FORMERLY ALL THE FOUR DIVISIONS* OF THE ARMY USED TO ATTEND ON RAMA. TODAY HE IS ONLY FOLLOWED BY SITA AND LAKSHMANA.

DID WE DECORATE THE CAPITAL ONLY TO SEND OUR PRINCE TO THE FOREST?

* INFANTRY, CAVALRY, CHARIOT-RIDERS, ELEPHANT RIDERS

RAMA IS VIRTUOUS, COMPASSIONATE, LEARNED, TRUTHFUL AND SELF-CONTROLLED...

...HOW COULD THE KING SEND SO DEAR A SON INTO EXILE!

WE WILL ABANDON OUR HOMES AND FOLLOW RAMA!

YES, WE WILL!

WHEN RAMA'S ARRIVAL WAS ANNOUNCED, THE OLD KING ROSE TO GREET HIM...

O, RAMA!

...BUT THE NEXT MINUTE HE FELL DOWN, SENSELESS.

RAMA RUSHED FORWARD, TOOK HIM IN HIS ARMS...

...AND PLACED HIM GENTLY ON THE COUCH.

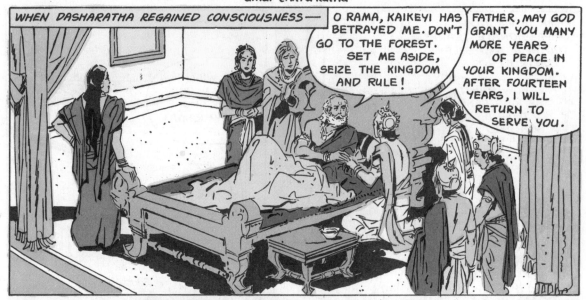

WHEN DASHARATHA REGAINED CONSCIOUSNESS—

O RAMA, KAIKEYI HAS BETRAYED ME. DON'T GO TO THE FOREST. SET ME ASIDE, SEIZE THE KINGDOM AND RULE!

FATHER, MAY GOD GRANT YOU MANY MORE YEARS OF PEACE IN YOUR KINGDOM. AFTER FOURTEEN YEARS, I WILL RETURN TO SERVE YOU.

PERMIT ME TO LEAVE NOW, FATHER, WITH SITA AND LAKSHMANA.

THEN TAKE MY WEALTH AND PEOPLE WITH YOU, RAMA. LET THE FOREST WHERE YOU DWELL BE THE KINGDOM!

OH, NO!

O KING! BHARATA WILL NOT ACCEPT A KINGDOM STRIPPED OF ITS WEALTH AND PEOPLE.

FATHER, WHAT NEED HAVE I OF WEALTH IN THE FOREST? THE TREES, CLOUDS, SPARKLING STREAMS — THOSE ARE WEALTH ENOUGH!

I'LL LEAD THE LIFE OF AN ASCETIC. GIVE ME ROBES OF BARK!

NO ONE MOVED —

NO, RAMA!

HOW CAN WE BEAR TO SEE OUR PRINCE ATTIRED IN BARK?

THEN KAIKEYI PERSONALLY FETCHED GARMENTS OF BARK.

HERE, PUT THESE ON.

RAMA AND LAKSHMANA CHANGED INTO THE ROBES OF BARK.

HOW DO WOMEN ASCETICS WEAR THESE ROBES?

I'LL SHOW YOU.

BUT VASISHTHA INTERVENED.

SITA IS NOT COMPELLED TO GO INTO EXILE. GOING OF HER OWN FREE WILL, IT IS ONLY BEFITTING THAT SHE SHOULD BE ATTIRED IN ROYAL DRESS. ALSO, LET HER KEEP HER ORNAMENTS AS WELL.

DASHARATHA UPHELD VASISHTHA'S CONTENTION. SITA BOWED TO THE WISHES OF THE ELDERS, AND ACCEPTED THE ORNAMENTS OFFERED BY DASHARATHA.

RAMA THEN SALUTED DASHARATHA AND THE QUEENS, AND LEFT THE PALACE WITH SITA AND LAKSHMANA. THEY STEPPED INTO THE CHARIOT WHICH WOULD TAKE THEM TO THE BORDERS OF THE KINGDOM.

RAMA!

SHEDDING TEARS, PEOPLE RAN AFTER THE CHARIOT WHILE THE OLD KING STOOD WATCHING HELPLESSLY.

O, CHARIOTEER, DRIVE SLOWLY! LET US BEHOLD RAMA AS LONG AS WE CAN!

PLEASE GO BACK! IF YOU REALLY LOVE ME, BESTOW THE LOVE AND HONOUR YOU SHOW TO ME ON BHARATA.

WE WILL FOLLOW YOU A LITTLE WHILE LONGER!

IT WAS NIGHT BY THE TIME THEY REACHED THE BANKS OF THE RIVER TAMASA. THERE THEY RESTED.

LAKSHMANA, LET US GO BEFORE THESE GOOD PEOPLE WAKE UP. OTHERWISE, THEY WILL NOT LEAVE US.

PROCEEDING SOUTHWARDS, RAMA, SITA AND LAKSHMANA CROSSED THE RIVERS TAMASA, VEDASHRUTI AND GOMATI...

...AND REACHED THE SOUTHERN BORDER OF KOSALA. THERE THEY ALIGHTED FROM THE CHARIOT. WITH HIS FACE TURNED TOWARDS AYODHYA, RAMA JOINED HIS PALMS TOGETHER IN SALUTATION.

O AYODHYA, I BID YOU FAREWELL! AFTER MY PLEDGE IS FULFILLED, I SHALL RETURN FROM THE FOREST AND BEHOLD YOU AND MY PARENTS AGAIN!

WHEN RAMA ARRIVED ON THE NORTHERN BANK OF THE RIVER GANGA, GUHA, THE CHIEF OF THE TRIBE OF HUNTERS INHABITING THE REGION, RECEIVED HIM.

O PRINCE, TELL ME HOW I CAN SERVE YOU.

PROVIDE ME WITH A BOAT TO CROSS OVER TO THE SOUTHERN BANK.

NEXT MORNING, RAMA RUBBED HIS HAIR WITH THE SAP OF THE BHURJA TREE AND LAKSHMANA DID THE SAME. LIKE ASCETICS THEY HAD NOW THEIR HAIR MATTED.

THE NEXT DAY —

SUMANTRA, IT IS TIME FOR YOU TO RETURN TO AYODHYA.

SUMANTRA'S EYES WERE FILLED WITH TEARS.

HOW CAN I RETURN WITH AN EMPTY CHARIOT? NO, RAMA, I WON'T GO BACK. I WILL ACCOMPANY YOU TO THE FOREST AND SERVE YOU!

SUMANTRA, IF YOU HAVE AFFECTION FOR ME, DO AS I SAY. GO BACK TO AYODHYA. CONSOLE MY FATHER AND ASSURE MOTHER KAIKEYI THAT I HAVE INDEED LEFT FOR THE FOREST.

SUMANTRA AGREED RELUCTANTLY. RAMA, SITA AND LAKSHMANA CROSSED THE RIVER IN THE BOAT PROVIDED BY GUHA.

THEY RESUMED THEIR JOURNEY THROUGH THE DENSE FOREST. WHEN THEY REACHED PRAYAG, WHERE THE GANGA AND THE YAMUNA MEET, THEY MET SAGE BHARADWAJA.

O, BLESSED SAGE, SUGGEST A SECLUDED PLACE WHERE WE MAY LIVE IN HAPPINESS.

O, CHILD, ACROSS THE YAMUNA IS THE MOUNTAIN CHITRAKUTA WHICH IS FILLED WITH FLOWERS AND FRUITS, SPRINGS AND WATERFALLS. THERE YOU WILL FIND AN IDEAL RETREAT.

SO RAMA WENT TO CHITRAKUTA, WHERE HE BUILT A HUT BY THE RIVER MANDAKINI. ONE DAY—

THE BIRDS ARE FRIGHTENED AND I SEE A CLOUD OF DUST IN THE DISTANCE. LAKSHMANA, PLEASE FIND OUT WHY.

LAKSHMANA CLIMBED UP A TREE AND LOOKED INTO THE DISTANCE.

RAMA, BE ON GUARD! HAVING SECURED THE THRONE, BHARATA IS BRINGING HIS ARMY HERE TO DEPRIVE US OF OUR LIVES!

THE VIRTUOUS BHARATA? NO, YOU'LL PRESENTLY SEE THAT YOU'VE WRONGED A NOBLE SOUL.

SOON —

RAMA!

BHARATA! SHATRUGHNA, YOU HERE, TOO!

HOW HASTY I AM IN JUDGING PEOPLE! BHARATA'S LOVE FOR RAMA IS AS GREAT AS MINE.

BHARATA, WHY ARE YOU DRESSED IN ASCETIC ROBES? WHAT NEWS FROM AYODHYA? IS OUR DEAR FATHER WELL?

O RAMA, FATHER COULD NOT BEAR THE SEPARATION FROM YOU! HE WANTED TO BEHOLD YOU AGAIN. THINKING OF YOU, CALLING OUT YOUR NAME...

RAMA... RAMA... RAMA...

...HE DIED WHILE I WAS YET AT MY GRANDFATHER'S HOUSE.

OH! FATHER! FATHER!

BHARATA, I WAS LOOKING FORWARD TO RETURNING TO AYODHYA AFTER MY EXILE. BUT I NO LONGER FEEL THE SAME EAGERNESS NOW THAT FATHER IS DEAD.

THEN RAMA OFFERED A LIBATION OF WATER TO HIS DEAD FATHER.

O KING, MAY THIS SACRED WATER OFFERED TODAY BE YOURS FOR EVER IN THE REGION OF OUR ANCESTORS!

SUMANTRA, VASISHTHA AND OTHER ELDERS WHO HAD BY THEN JOINED THEM CONSOLED RAMA. RAMA TURNED TO BHARATA.

YOU HAVEN'T ANSWERED MY QUESTION, BHARATA. WHY ARE YOU, TOO, DRESSED IN ASCETIC ROBES?

RAMA, WHEN THE LAWFUL SUCCESSOR TO THE THRONE IS LANGUISHING IN THE FOREST, HOW CAN I DON ROYAL ROBES?

THEN BHARATA OFFERED THE ROYAL ROBES AND SANDALS TO RAMA.

PLEASE PUT ON THESE KINGLY ROBES AND RETURN TO AYODHYA.

NO, BHARATA. I CANNOT DO THAT.

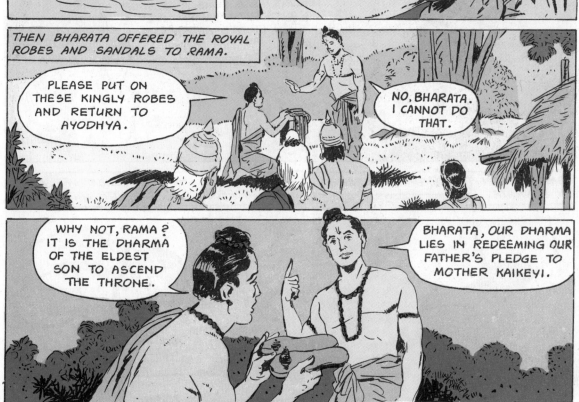

WHY NOT, RAMA? IT IS THE DHARMA OF THE ELDEST SON TO ASCEND THE THRONE.

BHARATA, OUR DHARMA LIES IN REDEEMING OUR FATHER'S PLEDGE TO MOTHER KAIKEYI.

THEN BHARATA APPEALED TO THE ELDERS.

IF, IN OBEDIENCE TO MY FATHER'S COMMAND, SOME— ONE MUST LIVE IN THE FOREST FOR FOURTEEN YEARS, THEN LET ME BE THE PERSON, INSTEAD OF RAMA.

BUT RAMA WOULD NOT YIELD.

THE ISSUE IS STRAIGHT. IN ACCORDANCE WITH THE BOON, YOU RULE AND I GO INTO EXILE FOR FOURTEEN YEARS.

BHARATA GAVE IN.

IN THAT CASE, I WILL RULE— BUT ONLY ON YOUR BEHALF. I WILL PLACE YOUR SANDALS ON THE THRONE AS A SYMBOL OF YOUR AUTHORITY. I WILL LIVE ON FRUITS AND ROOTS AS YOU DO.

RAMA PUT ON THE SANDALS OFFERED BY BHARATA.

AFTER A WHILE, HE TOOK THEM OFF, AND BHARATA RECEIVED THEM WITH DUE RESPECT.

THEN HE DEPARTED WITH A HEAVY HEART.

RAMA, I AWAIT WITH LONGING THE HAPPY DAY WHEN YOU WILL RETURN TO AYODHYA AT THE END OF YOUR EXILE.

RAMA EMBRACED BHARATA.

MEANWHILE, LOOK AFTER THE KINGDOM, BROTHER. PROTECT MOTHER KAIKEYI. DON'T BE ANGRY WITH HER.

THUS REASSURED BY RAMA, BHARATA LEFT.

THEN, ACCOMPANIED BY SITA AND LAKSHMANA, RAMA WENT TO THE DANDAKA FOREST WHERE HE KILLED THE RAKSHASA, VIRADHA.

SEVERAL SAGES LIVING IN THE FOREST MET RAMA.

WE ARE WITHOUT A PROTECTOR. DEFEND US FROM THE CRUEL PERSECUTION OF THE RAKSHASAS.

I WILL!

LATER, RAMA CALLED ON SAGE AGASTYA AND PAID HIS RESPECTS. THE SAGE GAVE HIM CELESTIAL WEAPONS.

HOLY ONE, I AM GRATEFUL TO YOU FOR YOUR KINDNESS. PLEASE SUGGEST A PLACE WHERE I CAN DWELL WITH MY WIFE AND BROTHER!

GO TO PANCHAVATI, EIGHT MILES AWAY, AND LIVE THERE HAPPILY.

ON THE WAY TO PANCHAVATI, AN AGED VULTURE ADDRESSED HIM —

O RAMA! I AM JATAYU, A FRIEND OF YOUR FATHER'S. I WILL STAY AROUND WITH YOU IN CASE YOU NEED MY HELP.

THANK YOU. YOUR PRESENCE WILL BE A COMFORT.

WHEN RAMA REACHED PANCHAVATI —

THIS IS THE PERFECT SPOT TO BUILD OUR COTTAGE.

LAKSHMANA BEGAN TO BUILD AN ASHRAM* FOR HIS BROTHER.

WHEN IT WAS READY, HE BATHED IN THE HOLY GODAVARI. HE PRAYED TO THE GODS AND PLACED A LOTUS ON THE THRESHOLD OF THE COTTAGE AS AN OFFERING TO THEM.

THEN HE SHOWED THE ASHRAM TO RAMA.

IT'S WONDERFUL. THE ONLY WAY I CAN REWARD YOU IS BY...

... EMBRACING YOU.

* FOREST RETREAT

THE ASHRAM WAS SPACIOUS AND COMFORTABLE. THE SPENT MANY HAPPY DAYS THERE. ONE DAY, SHOORPANAKHA, A RAKSHASI, WHO WAS PASSING THROUGH PANCHAVATI, SAW RAMA.

WHAT A HANDSOME MAN! I WOULD LIKE TO MARRY HIM.

ASSUMING A BEAUTIFUL FORM, SHE APPROACHED RAMA.

O, ASCETIC, ARMED WITH BOW AND ARROW, WHY HAVE YOU COME TO THIS REGION OF THE RAKSHASAS?

I AM RAMA, THE SON OF KING DASHARATHA, AND FOR FOURTEEN YEARS I HAVE TO LIVE IN EXILE IN THIS FOREST.

I AM SHOORPANAKHA, SISTER OF THE MIGHTY RAVANA. KHARA AND DOOSHANA OF MATCH- LESS STRENGTH, WHO RULE JANASTHANA ARE MY BROTHERS....

...O PRINCE, MARRY ME. MY BEAUTY MATCHES YOURS.

RAMA SMILED AND REPLIED IN A MOCKING TONE.

I AM ALREADY MARRIED. BUT, LOOK, HERE IS MY BROTHER, LAKSHMANA. HE IS WORTHY OF YOU, O BEAUTIFUL ONE!

YOU ARE A PRINCESS AND I AM ONLY RAMA'S SLAVE. WOULD IT BE PROPER FOR YOU TO MARRY ME?

NO!

ANGRILY, SHOORPANAKHA TURNED TO RAMA.

ARE YOU SPURNING ME BECAUSE OF YOUR UGLY WIFE?

I'LL DEVOUR HER. THEN WILL YOU MARRY ME?

AS SHE RUSHED TOWARDS SITA —

STOP HER, LAKSHMANA!

LAKSHMANA LEAPT AT HER AND CUT OFF HER EARS AND NOSE. SHOORPANAKHA REGAINED HER TRUE FORM AND FLED.

NOT LONG AFTER, SHOORPANAKHA RETURNED TO PANCHAVATI WITH DOOSHANA, KHARA AND FOURTEEN THOUSAND RAKSHASAS.

LAKSHMANA, LEAVE THE RAKSHASAS TO ME! YOU TAKE SITA AWAY FROM HERE INTO THE SHELTER OF THAT CAVE!

THE NEXT MOMENT, RAMA WAS SURROUNDED BY RAKSHASAS —

AND HE KILLED THEM ALL SINGLE-HANDED...

...EXCEPT FOR AKAMPANA, WHO MANAGED TO ESCAPE. AKAMPANA FLEW OVER THE SOUTHERN OCEAN...

...AND REACHED LANKA, WHERE RULED RAVANA, THE MIGHTY KING OF RAKSHASAS.

O KING, YOUR VALIANT BROTHERS, KHARA AND DOOSHANA, HAVE BEEN SLAIN BY RAMA, THE PRINCE OF AYODHYA.

MY BROTHERS KILLED BY A MERE MAN!

HE HAS INVITED HIS OWN DESTRUCTION BY KILLING MY BROTHERS! I'LL SLAY HIM!

O MIGHTY ONE, NOT EVEN THE GODS CAN OVERCOME RAMA!

THE ONLY WAY TO DESTROY HIM IS TO CARRY AWAY HIS BEAUTIFUL WIFE, SITA. BEREFT OF HER WHOM HE LOVES DEARLY HE WILL CERTAINLY DIE OF A BROKEN HEART!

LET ME CONSULT MARICHA.

RAVANA CALLED ON MARICHA WHO WAS NOW LEADING AN ASCETIC LIFE.

RAVANA, HE WHO HAS ADVISED YOU TO CARRY AWAY SITA IS AN ENEMY IN THE GUISE OF A FRIEND.

MARICHA THEN RECALLED HIS OWN ENCOUNTER WITH RAMA.

DON'T ANTAGONISE RAMA WHO HUNTS DEMONS AS HE WOULD DEER.

I'D BETTER TAKE YOUR ADVICE.

WHEN HE RETURNED HOME, RAVANA FOUND SHOORPANAKHA WAITING FOR HIM.

BROTHER, LOOK AT YOUR DEAR SISTER MUTILATED BY THAT MAN FROM AYODHYA! IF YOU DON'T AVENGE THE DEATH OF KHARA AND DOOSHANA, BOTH THE GODS AND HUMANS WILL CEASE TO FEAR THE RAKSHASAS! YOU MUST ACT AT ONCE!

RAVANA WENT TO MARICHA AGAIN TO SEEK HIS HELP IN ABDUCTING SITA—

O KING, THERE IS NO GREATER SIN THAN COVETING ANOTHER MAN'S WIFE! LEAVE SITA ALONE.

YOU REFUSE? THEN YOU SHALL FEEL THE KEEN EDGE OF MY BLADE!

I'LL DO WHAT YOU ASK. BUT, REMEMBER, THOSE FOR WHOM THE LAST HOUR HAS STRUCK DISREGARD THE COUNSEL OF THEIR WELL-WISHERS.

MEANWHILE, AT PANCHAVATI, RAMA AND SITA RESUMED THEIR QUIET LIFE. THE UNPLEASANT EPISODE WITH SHOORPANAKHA WAS FORGOTTEN.

RAMA, LOOK AT THAT BEAUTIFUL FLOWER! IT HAS JUST OPENED ITS FACE TO THE SUN!

YES, YOU SHOWED IT TO ME YESTERDAY, WHEN IT WAS JUST A BUD!

JUST THEN, RAVANA AND MARICHA HAD ARRIVED AT PANCHAVATI.

OH, SHE IS QUITE LOVELY!

MARICHA, YOUR TASK IS TO LURE RAMA AND LAKSHMANA AWAY FROM THE COTTAGE.

THE NEXT MOMENT —

OH! LOOK! WHAT A LOVELY DEER!

THAT DEER IS TOO WONDERFUL TO BE REAL. LOOK, HOW IT SHINES! IT COULD ONLY BE A RAKSHASA!

IGNORING LAKSHMANA'S WORDS, SITA CONTINUED —

ISN'T IT BEAUTIFUL, RAMA! WILL YOU GET IT FOR ME?

CERTAINLY, MY DEAR!

LAKSHMANA, I'LL BRING THAT DEER BACK ALIVE. IF IT IS A RAKSHASA IN DISGUISE, I'LL SLAY HIM. YOU STAY HERE AND GUARD SITA.

RAMA SET OUT IN PURSUIT OF THE DEER.

SITA AND LAKSHMANA WAITED A LONG TIME BUT RAMA STILL DID NOT RETURN.

THE SWIFT-FOOTED DEER MUST HAVE LED HIM FAR.

RAMA WILL GET THE DEER, DEAD OR ALIVE.

SUDDENLY —

O SITA... O LAKSHMANA...

MY LORD!

IT IS MY LORD CRYING FOR HELP. LAKSHMANA! RUSH TO HIS AID. HE MUST BE IN DANGER!

LAKSHMANA WAS UNPERTURBED.

HE CAN'T BE. RAMA IS INVINCIBLE. IT MUST BE A RAKSHASA MIMICKING HIM. I WON'T LEAVE YOUR SIDE.

BUT SITA WAS NOT CONVINCED.

GO, LAKSHMANA! PLEASE GO! HELP MY HUSBAND!

I CAN'T GO. I CAN'T LEAVE YOU HERE UNPROTECTED.

RAVANA THEN WENT TOWARDS SITA IN THE GUISE OF AN ASCETIC.

GOOD LADY, YOU LIVE HERE ALONE? IN THIS FOREST WHICH IS FULL OF RAKSHASAS AND WILD ANIMALS?

SITA OFFERED HIM WATER TO WASH HIS FEET, AND FRUIT TO EAT.

MY LORD, RAMA, HAS GONE TO CAPTURE A DEER FOR ME. HE WILL RETURN SOON.

O SITA, I'M RAVANA, KING OF THE RAKSHASAS. FORGET RAMA AND COME WITH ME TO MY GREAT KINGDOM, LANKA. THERE YOU SHALL BE MY QUEEN!

I AM RAMA'S CONSORT AND HIS ALONE! VILE MAN, TO CARRY ME AWAY WOULD BE LIKE TAKING A BLAZING FIRE IN YOUR GARMENTS!

RAMA IS MY INFERIOR IN COMBAT. ACCEPT ME AS YOUR LORD!

O, RAKSHASA, HE WHO INSULTS A CHASTE LADY WILL NEVER ESCAPE DEATH EVEN IF HE DRINKS THE NECTAR OF IMMORTALITY.

HAVEN'T YOU HEARD OF MY VALOUR? I CAN LIFT THE EARTH, PIERCE THE SUN AND DESTROY DEATH HIMSELF IN COMBAT!

INFLAMED BY SITA'S BEAUTY AND ANGERED BY HER REJECTION OF HIM, RAVANA ASSUMED HIS TRUE FORM AND DRAGGED SITA OUT OF THE COTTAGE.

SURRENDER TO A MASTER FAMED THROUGHOUT THE THREE WORLDS!

O RAMA! O RAMA....

RAVANA CARRIED SITA TO HIS CHARIOT AND BEGAN SPEEDING THROUGH THE SKY TOWARDS LANKA.

O, RAMA...! O, LAKSHMANA...!

MEANWHILE IN ANOTHER PART OF THE FOREST—

LAKSHMANA! YOU'RE HERE ALONE! WHERE'S SITA?

RAMA, WE HEARD YOU CRY OUT FOR HELP. SITA INSISTED THAT I LEAVE HER AND COME TO YOUR RESCUE.

I DID NOT CRY OUT! AS YOU SUSPECTED, THE DEER WAS NO ORDINARY DEER. IT WAS MARICHA, THE RAKSHASA.

"I CHASED HIM AND, THOUGH HE WAS SWIFT AS THE WIND, I FINALLY SHOT HIM DOWN. WHEN MY ARROW STRUCK HIM, HIS TRUE FORM BECAME APPARENT."

THEN, MIMICKING MY VOICE WITH HIS DYING BREATH HE CALLED OUT YOUR NAME AND SITA'S !

I KNEW IT WAS NOT YOU ! BUT SITA WAS DISTRACTED BY FEAR AND FORCED ME TO COME !

ANYWAY, THE RAKSHASA HAS BEEN KILLED. LET'S HURRY BACK !

LAKSHMANA, CAN ALL BE WELL ? SITA IS NOT HERE TO GREET US !

WHEN THE TWO REACHED THE ASHRAM, AN OMINOUS SILENCE GREETED THEM.

SITA !

BUT SITA WAS NOT THERE. OVERCOME BY GRIEF, RAMA ADDRESSED THE TREES IN THE ASHRAM.

O KADAMBA YOUR FLOWERS WERE ADMIRED BY MY BELOVED. HAVE YOU SEEN HER? TELL ME WHERE SHE IS!

O ASHOKA, TALA, SHALA, VISHALA, BAKULA, CHANDANA, WHERE IS MY SITA?

SUDDENLY—

WHY ARE YOU RUNNING AWAY FROM ME, MY BELOVED? I HAVE SEEN YOU!

STOP! ENOUGH OF FUN, SITA! DON'T YOU SEE I'M SUFFERING? COME BACK, MY BELOVED!

THE NEXT MOMENT—

NO, IT WAS AN ILLUSION! MY SITA IS NOT ALIVE!

DON'T GIVE UP HOPE SO QUICKLY. SITA MAY HAVE VENTURED DEEP INTO THE FOREST OR GONE TO THE RIVER.

THEY SEARCHED FOR A LONG TIME — BUT IT WAS IN VAIN.

O, SITA! HOW SHALL I EXPLAIN YOUR ABSENCE TO YOUR FATHER WHEN I RETURN FROM EXILE?

I WILL NOT RETURN. AFTER OUR PERIOD OF EXILE, YOU MUST GO BACK TO AYODHYA WITHOUT ME, LAKSHMANA.

WE WILL FIND SITA! I AM CERTAIN WE WILL!

O SUN, YOU WITNESS EVERYTHING THAT TAKES PLACE ON EARTH. TELL ME, HAS MY BELOVED WANDERED AWAY OR HAS SHE BEEN ABDUCTED?

RAMA CONTINUED HIS SEARCH, ASKING RIVERS, TREES AND ANIMALS THE SAME QUESTION —

O DEER, SITA LOVED YOU. TELL ME WHERE SHE IS!

RAMA, THE DEER KEEPS LOOKING SOUTHWARDS. LET'S GO IN THAT DIRECTION!

WHEN THE BROTHERS PROCEEDED SOUTHWARDS, RAMA FOUND SOME FLOWERS SCATTERED ON THE GROUND.

LOOK LAKSHMANA! THESE ARE THE FLOWERS I HAD GATHERED FOR SITA. THE SUN, THE WIND AND THE EARTH HAVE PRESERVED THEM FOR ME!

A LITTLE FURTHER —

THESE ARE SITA'S FOOTPRINTS! BUT WHAT ARE THESE? GIANT FOOT-PRINTS!

AND THESE ARE SOME OF HER ORNAMENTS!

A SHATTERED CHARIOT, A BROKEN BOW, DEAD MULES AND A CHARIOTEER KILLED! WHAT'S THIS? A BATTLE FOUGHT FOR SITA?

THE NEXT MOMENT, RAMA FLEW INTO AN UNCONTROLLABLE RAGE.

MY BELOVED HAS BEEN TAKEN AWAY FROM ME! IF THE GODS DO NOT RESTORE HER TO ME NOW, I'LL DESTROY THE WHOLE WORLD!

AS RAMA PREPARED TO RELEASE HIS TERRIBLE ARROW —

WAIT!

DON'T DESTROY THE WORLD FOR ONE MAN'S SIN! SEEK OUT YOUR TORMENTOR AND PUNISH HIM, BY ALL MEANS. BUT SPARE INNOCENT LIVES.

THUS PACIFIED, RAMA WITHDREW THE ARROW AND PROCEEDED FURTHER. SUDDENLY —

THAT RAKSHASA, THERE IN THE FORM OF A VULTURE! HAVING DEVOURED MY BELOVED, HE IS NOW RESTING. WRETCH! I WILL KILL YOU!

THEN HE STOPPED IN SUR —

IT IS JATAYU! AND HE IS HURT!

O, RAMA, I SAW SITA BEING CARRIED AWAY BY RAVANA!

"I KILLED HIS CHARIOTEER AND MULES...

...AND SHATTERED HIS CHARIOT. RAVANA JUMPED TO THE GROUND, CARRYING SITA WITH HIM.

LEAVING SITA THERE, RAVANA ROSE INTO THE SKY AGAIN.

CHILD, RUN AWAY TO SAFETY. I'LL DEAL WITH THIS WRETCH!

RAVANA STRUCK ME. HE SEVERED MY WINGS AND CLAWS.

AS I FELL DOWN BLEEDING, SITA CAME RUNNING BACK TO ME."

WITH A SIGH, JATAYU CONCLUDED HIS TALE.

JUST THEN, RAVANA SEIZED HER AND CARRIED HER AWAY SOUTHWARDS.

O NOBLE BIRD, TELL ME, WHO IS THIS RAVANA?

GASPING FOR BREATH, JATAYU SPOKE HALTINGLY.

RAVANA, IS THE... KING OF...RAKSHASAS... SON OF...VISHRAVA....

SPEAK...SPEAK FURTHER!

BUT JATAYU HAD BREATHED HIS LAST.

RAMA WAS FULL OF GRIEF AT JATAYU'S DEATH.

O BEST OF BIRDS, I BOW TO YOU! I HOLD YOU IN EQUAL VENERATION WITH MY DEPARTED FATHER!

AFTER CREMATING THE NOBLE BIRD, THE BROTHERS RESUMED THEIR SEARCH.

WHEN THEY ENTERED THE KRAUNCHA FOREST, A RAKSHASA SEIZED THEM.

O RAMA! HOW SHALL WE ESCAPE FROM THIS RAKSHASA?

AS THE RAKSHASA OPENED HIS MOUTH TO SWALLOW THEM...

...THE TWO PRINCES SEVERED HIS HAND AND WERE JUST ABOUT TO ESCAPE...

...WHEN THE RAKSHASA SPOKE—

O, VALIANT BROTHERS, BURN ME AT ONCE, AND I'LL BE ABLE TO HELP YOU!

THEY BURNT THE RAKSHASA AND, OUT OF THE FLAMES, THERE AROSE A BEAUTIFUL FORM.

O, RAMA, MY NAME IS KABANDHA. A CURSE HAD REDUCED ME TO THAT LOATHSOME FORM FROM WHICH YOU HAVE RELEASED ME.

SEEK THE MONKEY-CHIEF, SUGREEVA. HE WILL HELP YOU FIND YOUR WIFE. HE LIVES ON RISHYA-MUKA MOUNTAIN.

THE TWO BROTHERS MOVED ON. WHEN THEY REACHED THE WESTERN BANK OF LAKE PAMPA, THE AGED ASCETIC, SHABARI, RECEIVED THEM.

AT LAST MY DEAREST WISH HAS BEEN GRANTED, O RAMA! I HAVE BEEN LIVING ONLY FOR THIS MOMENT!

PLEASE PARTAKE OF THIS FRUIT WHICH I HAVE GATHERED FOR YOU!

THIS FRUIT IS THE SWEETEST ON EARTH!

SOON AFTER, SHABARI ABANDONED HER MORTAL BODY AND ATTAINED SALVATION.

RESUMING THEIR JOURNEY, RAMA AND LAKSHMANA CROSSED THE LAKE PAMPA. AS THEY APPROACHED RISHYAMUKA MOUNTAIN, A MENDICANT MET THEM.

YOU ARE STRANGERS HERE. WHERE HAVE YOU COME FROM?

ER...ER...

SEEING THEIR HESITATION, HE CONTINUED—

DON'T BE AFRAID. SUGREEVA, THE KING OF THE MONKEYS, DESIRES YOUR FRIENDSHIP. I AM HANUMAN, HIS MINISTER.

O, HANUMAN, WE HAVE HEARD OF SUGREEVA'S VALOUR. IN FACT, WE HAVE COME IN SEARCH OF HIM.

LAKSHMANA THEN TOLD HANUMAN ABOUT RAMA'S EXILE AND SITA'S ABDUCTION.

MY KING, SUGREEVA, TOO, IS AN EXILE. HIS BROTHER, VALI, TREATED HIM CRUELLY, FORCING HIM TO FLEE FROM KISHKINDHA, THE MONKEY-KINGDOM. SUGREEVA WILL MAKE A PACT OF FRIENDSHIP WITH YOU.

HANUMAN ASSUMED HIS TRUE FORM AND CARRIED THEM...

...TO RISHYAMUKA MOUNTAIN WHERE SUGREEVA LIVED. AFTER HANUMAN HAD RELATED RAMA'S STORY—

INDEED, I AM FORTUNATE THAT YOU SEEK MY FRIENDSHIP!

WITH FIRE AS WITNESS, RAMA AND SUGREEVA WERE UNITED IN FRIENDSHIP.

YOU ARE NOW MY FRIEND. IN JOY AND SORROW, WE ARE ONE.

SUGREEVA, I WILL HELP YOU REGAIN YOUR KINGDOM.

RAMA, I WILL HELP YOU GET BACK YOUR WIFE BE SHE HIDDEN IN HEAVEN OR IN THE NETHER WORLD!

WE SAW SITA BEING CARRIED AWAY. SHE WAS CALLING OUT YOUR NAME AND SHE EVEN THREW DOWN HER JEWELS WHICH WE HAVE PRESERVED.

BRING THEM TO ME QUICKLY, DEAR FRIEND!

SUGREEVA BROUGHT SITA'S JEWELS FROM THE CAVE. RAMA TOOK THEM GENTLY.

O SITA!

HE SHOWED THEM TO LAKSHMANA.

O LAKSHMANA, DON'T YOU RECOGNISE SITA'S ORNAMENTS?

I DON'T RECOGNISE THE BRACELET AND EAR-RINGS, BUT I DO KNOW THESE ANKLETS FOR I WORSHIPPED HER FEET ALONE.

LATER, SUGREEVA CHALLENGED HIS WICKED BROTHER VALI TO FIGHT HIM. ALTHOUGH BADLY BEATEN EARLIER HE FOUGHT AGAIN, CONFIDENT THAT RAMA WOULD PLAY HIS PART AT THE RIGHT TIME.

RAMA'S ARROW FOUND ITS MARK AND VALI WAS SLAIN.

RAMA CROWNED SUGREEVA THE KING OF KISHKINDHA. UNFORTUNATELY, FORGETTING HIS DUTY TO RAMA, THE KING GAVE HIMSELF UP TO A LIFE OF PLEASURE. THEN HANUMAN GENTLY REBUKED HIS KING.

O KING, YOU OWE YOUR PROSPERITY TO RAMA. REDEEM YOUR PLEDGE AND HELP TO FIND HIS WIFE.

REPENTANT, SUGREEVA'S SENSE OF DUTY WAS AROUSED. HE CALLED A MEETING OF THE MONKEYS.

MY LOYAL SOLDIERS, I WANT YOU TO SPREAD OUT AND GO IN DIFFERENT DIRECTIONS IN SEARCH OF SITA!

BEFORE HANUMAN SET OUT, RAMA GAVE HIM A RING.

IF ANYONE CAN FIND SITA IT IS YOU, HANUMAN. TAKE THIS RING! IT WILL BE A SIGN TO HER THAT YOU ARE MY MESSENGER.

HANUMAN WENT SOUTHWARDS ACCOMPANIED BY ANGADA, THE CROWN PRINCE OF KISHKINDHA; JAMBAVAN, THE AGED AND WISE BEAR; AND MONKEYS OF GREAT STRENGTH.

THOUGH THEY SEARCHED CAREFULLY AND LONG, THEY COULD NOT FIND ANY TRACE OF SITA.

WHAT SHALL WE DO?

THIS IS A FRUITLESS SEARCH! WE'LL NEVER FIND SITA!

THEN THEY NOTICED THE VULTURE, SAMPATI, BROTHER OF JATAYU, WHO HAD BEEN WATCHING THEM.

ARE YOU LOOKING FOR SITA? I SAW RAVANA CARRYING HER ACROSS THE OCEAN TO HIS ISLAND KINGDOM, LANKA.

SO HANUMAN AND HIS ARMY RESUMED THEIR JOURNEY. WHEN THEY REACHED THE SOUTHERN OCEAN, THEY WERE FILLED WITH DISMAY.

THIS VAST STRETCH OF OCEAN LIES BETWEEN US AND LANKA. HOW SHALL WE GET ACROSS!

IT'S IMPOSSIBLE! WE CAN'T GET TO LANKA!

THERE MUST BE A WAY! PERHAPS ONE OF US COULD JUMP ACROSS AND DEAL WITH RAVANA.

WHO WILL DO IT? WHO CAN JUMP THE FARTHEST?

I CAN LEAP THREE HUNDRED YOJANAS*!

I, FOUR HUNDRED!

I, FIVE HUNDRED!

BUT THERE WAS NO ONE AMONG THEM WHO COULD JUMP FAR ENOUGH, EXCEPT HANUMAN. JAMBAVAN, THE AGED BEAR APPROACHED HIM.

O HANUMAN, ONLY YOU CAN CROSS THE OCEAN! WHY ARE YOU SILENT? DON'T YOU KNOW YOUR OWN POWER?

* ONE YOJANA IS EQUAL TO THIRTEEN KILOMETRES

WHEN YOU WERE BUT A CHILD, YOU LEAPT TO SEIZE THE RISING SUN MISTAKING IT FOR A FRUIT!

COME, HANUMAN, LEAP ACROSS THE MIGHTY OCEAN! NO ONE CAN SURPASS YOU IN STRENGTH AND SPEED!

YES, JAMBAVAN. I WILL FLY TO LANKA.

THEN HANUMAN, THE SON OF THE WIND-GOD, ASSUMED A HUGE FORM...

...AND LEAPED INTO THE SKY.

HANUMAN FLEW AT A GREAT SPEED.

SUDDENLY, A HUGE MOUNTAIN ROSE UP FROM THE OCEAN. HANUMAN STRUCK IT HARD ...

...AND THE PEAK ASSUMED THE FORM OF A HUMAN FACE.

I AM MOUNT MAINAKA. YOUR FATHER ONCE HELPED ME. REST HERE A WHILE FOR YOU HAVE A LONG WAY TO GO.

THANK YOU, BUT I CAN'T REST TILL MY MISSION IS ACCOMPLISHED.

HANUMAN HAD BARELY FLOWN PAST MOUNT MAINAKA WHEN A NEW DANGER CONFRONTED HIM. SURASA, MOTHER OF SERPENTS, WHO HAD ASSUMED THE TERRIBLE FORM OF A SEA MONSTER TO TEST HANUMAN, WAITED FOR HIM WITH BURNING RAGE!

NO ONE CAN PASS ME WITHOUT ENTERING MY MOUTH. AND ONCE YOU ENTER, YOU CAN'T GET OUT ALIVE. SO PREPARE TO DIE!

BUT CAN YOUR MOUTH HOLD ME?

HANUMAN BEGAN TO INCREASE IN SIZE, BUT THE MONSTER ONLY OPENED HER JAWS WIDER AND WIDER.

SUDDENLY, HANUMAN REDUCED HIMSELF TO THE SIZE OF A THUMB AND, ENTERING HER MOUTH, FLASHED OUT AGAIN!

MEANWHILE, A RAKSHASI, SIMHIKA, WHO WAS LOOKING FOR FOOD, SPIED HIS SHADOW AS HE FLEW PAST HER.

AH! I CAN NOW HAVE A GOOD MEAL!

SIMHIKA SEIZED AT HIS SHADOW.

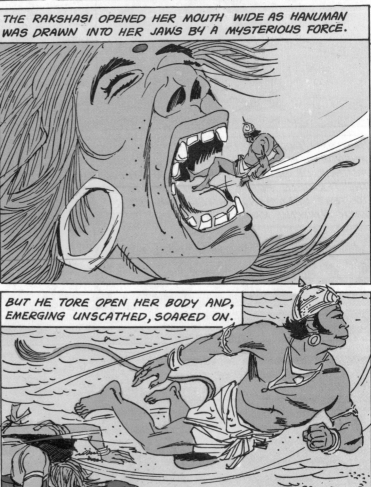

THE RAKSHASI OPENED HER MOUTH WIDE AS HANUMAN WAS DRAWN INTO HER JAWS BY A MYSTERIOUS FORCE.

BUT HE TORE OPEN HER BODY AND, EMERGING UNSCATHED, SOARED ON.

WHEN, AT LAST, HE REACHED LANKA AND WAS ABOUT TO ENTER UNDER COVER OF DARKNESS, THE GUARDIAN DEITY OF THE CITY BARRED THE WAY.

FOOLHARDY CREATURE! HOW DARE YOU ENTER THIS CITY WHEN I AM HERE TO PROTECT IT?

THERE! THAT WILL TAKE CARE OF HER FOR THE MOMENT!

IT HAS BEEN FORETOLD THAT THE RAKSHASAS WILL CEASE TO BE INVINCIBLE WHEN I AM OVERCOME BY A MONKEY! I FEAR THAT DAY HAS COME!

HANUMAN LEAPT OVER THE WALL AND ENTERED LANKA.

HOW SHALL I FIND RAMA'S CONSORT IN THIS VAST CITY?

HE WALKED THROUGH THE GOLDEN CITY OF LANKA TILL, AT LAST, HE CAME TO THE PALACE.

THIS MUST BE SITA!

NO, IT CAN'T BE SITA! SEPARATED FROM RAMA WOULD SHE BE ABLE TO SLEEP? OR EAT? WOULD SHE YIELD TO RAVANA? THIS MUST BE SOME OTHER LADY — ONE OF RAVANA'S QUEENS, PERHAPS.

HANUMAN LEFT THE PALACE. ON REACHING A NEARBY GROVE, HE CLIMBED THE TALLEST TREE.

WILL I FIND RAMA'S CONSORT IN THIS GROVE?

ALL THROUGH THE NIGHT, HE WANDERED SADLY ABOUT THE GROVE. AT DAY-BREAK —

I THINK I HAVE FOUND HER! THERE SHE IS, THINKING ONLY OF RAMA!

IT WAS INDEED SITA HELD CAPTIVE IN THE ASHOKA GROVE, GUARDED BY THE RAKSHASIS.

JUST THEN RAVANA ENTERED THE GROVE.

SHE TURNS A DEAF EAR TO MY WORDS OF LOVE. AND THREATS HAVE NO EFFECT ON HER. YET I KEEP HOPING THAT SHE WILL AGREE TO BE MINE ONE DAY!

O SITA, WHY DO YOU PINE FOR A HUSBAND WHO IS NOT MY MATCH IN STRENGTH, PROWESS, WEALTH OR FAME? YOU HAVE NO CHOICE. SOONER OR LATER YOU'LL HAVE TO AGREE TO BE MY QUEEN.

SITA, HER THOUGHTS FIXED ON RAMA, PLACED A STRAW BETWEEN RAVANA AND HERSELF.

JUST AS YOU CANNOT SEPARATE THE SUN FROM SUNLIGHT, YOU CANNOT SEPARATE RAMA FROM ME. IF YOU VALUE YOUR LIFE, RESTORE ME TO MY LORD AND SEEK HIS PROTECTION!

MY SWEET WORDS HAVE EARNED YOUR WRATH, NOT YOUR LOVE. I WON'T STAND YOUR ARROGANCE ANY LONGER!

SITA, I'LL GIVE YOU TWO MONTHS. THEN, IF YOU DON'T YIELD, MY COOKS WILL MINCE YOUR LIMBS FOR MY MORNING MEAL!

WHEN RAVANA LEFT, SEETHING WITH ANGER, THE RAKSHASIS TURNED TO SITA.

WHY DON'T YOU MAKE OUR LORD HAPPY?

HOW DARE YOU REFUSE HIM AGAIN AND AGAIN?

AGREE TO MARRY HIM!

NO! I WON'T AGREE. EVEN IF YOU THREATEN TO DEVOUR ME!

THAT'S A GOOD IDEA! WHY DON'T WE JUST DEVOUR HER?

THAT WILL SOLVE RAVANA'S PROBLEMS TOO!

WE CAN JUST SAY SHE DIED!

THE RAKSHASIS DRIFTED AWAY, DISCUSSING THE MATTER LOUDLY.

HAPPY ARE THOSE WHO ARE ABLE TO BEHOLD MY LORD. SHALL I EVER BE REUNITED WITH HIM?

SITA UNTIED THE CORD THAT HELD HER HAIR TOGETHER.

NO, I HAVE NO ALTERNATIVE. I'LL DO AWAY WITH MY LIFE WITH THE HELP OF THIS CORD.

HANUMAN HAD, BY NOW, REACHED THE BRANCHES ABOVE SITA.

THE GRIEF-STRICKEN SITA IS NOT HERSELF. IF I MAKE MY APPEARANCE BEFORE HER NOW, SHE MAY MISTAKE ME FOR RAVANA IN DISGUISE. I MUST WIN HER CONFIDENCE FIRST. I WILL SPEAK TO HER OF RAMA'S EXPLOITS.

HANUMAN BEGAN TO SPEAK SOFTLY ABOUT RAMA.

AT THE COMMAND OF HIS FATHER, RAMA, THE PRINCE OF AYODHYA, LEFT FOR THE FOREST ACCOMPANIED BY HIS CONSORT, SITA, AND HIS BROTHER, LAKSHMANA....

WHO IS THAT TALKING ABOUT MY LORD IN THIS COUNTRY OF RAKSHASAS?

...IN THE FOREST, RAVANA CARRIED SITA AWAY. THOUSANDS OF MONKEYS, FRIENDS OF RAMA, SET OUT TO SEARCH FOR SITA AND I HAVE FOUND HER HERE AT LAST!

OH! IT'S A MONKEY!

THE NEXT MOMENT—

IT MUST BE AN ILLUSION. I HEAR AND I SEE ONLY THOSE THINGS RELATED TO RAMA!

BUT HANUMAN CONTINUED TO SPEAK ABOUT RAMA TO ALLAY HER FEARS.

I AM HANUMAN, RAMA'S MESSENGER. HERE IS THE RING HE GAVE ME FOR YOU. CAN YOU TRUST ME NOW?

SITA EAGERLY TOOK THE RING.

I AM OVERCOME WITH JOY TO BEHOLD MY LORD'S RING!

IS RAMA VERY ANXIOUS ON MY ACCOUNT? DOES HE CONTINUE TO CARE FOR ME? WILL HE RESCUE ME? WILL HE STRIKE DOWN THIS VILE CREATURE WHO WISHES TO DEFILE ME?

RAMA WILL RESCUE YOU. NOTHING ELSE OCCUPIES HIS MIND. BUT NO ONE KNEW WHERE YOU WERE AND HE SENT ME AHEAD TO FIND OUT.

I WILL GO BACK AND TELL HIM YOU ARE HERE AND HE WILL COME AT ONCE TO RESCUE YOU. OR, PERHAPS, I COULD JUST CARRY YOU ON MY BACK TO RAMA.

NO, HANUMAN. RAMA WILL COME AND DESTROY RAVANA AND TAKE ME AWAY FROM HERE. ONLY THAT WILL VINDICATE MY HONOUR.

TAKING OUT A JEWEL WHICH SHE HAD CONCEALED IN HER CLOTHES, SHE OFFERED IT TO HANUMAN

GIVE THIS TO MY LORD.

ASK HIM TO RESCUE ME FROM THE CRUEL AND WICKED RAVANA.

RAMA WILL BE HERE SOON. RAVANA WILL FALL BY RAMA'S ARROW AND YOU WILL BE REUNITED WITH YOUR LORD!

NOW I MUST FIND OUT WHAT THE STRENGTH OF THE ENEMY IS. I SHOULD FIND A WAY OF MEETING RAVANA TO DISCOVER WHAT HE HAS IN MIND.

TO ATTRACT ATTENTION, HE BEGAN TO UPROOT THE TREES OF THE ASHOKA GROVE.

CAPTURE THAT MONKEY!

HANUMAN DEFEATED NOT ONLY THE GUARDS BUT ALSO THE ARMY WHICH FOLLOWED CLOSE BEHIND.

HANUMAN KILLED MANY RAKSHASA WARRIORS. AT LAST, RAVANA'S SON, THE MIGHTY INDRAJIT, CAME HIMSELF.

BUT EVEN INDRAJIT'S ARROWS COULD NOT TOUCH HANUMAN, FOR HE KEPT ON LEAPING HIGH IN THE AIR.

FINALLY, INDRAJIT INVOKED THE POWERFUL BRAHMA ASTRA WHICH ENABLED HIM TO BIND HANUMAN.

TAKE HIM AWAY!

HA! I RECEIVED A BOON FROM BRAHMA HIMSELF BY WHICH I CAN BE FREE. BUT I WILL NOT USE IT. I MUST MEET RAVANA.

HANUMAN WAS LED TO RAVANA'S COURT—

O RAVANA, I AM HANUMAN, A MESSENGER FROM KING SUGREEVA! YOU HAVE BEEN ENJOYING THE FRUITS OF YOUR MERITORIOUS ACTS SO FAR BUT SOON YOU WILL PAY FOR YOUR EVIL DEEDS UNLESS YOU RESTORE SITA TO RAMA.

IMPUDENT MONKEY! PUT HIM TO DEATH!

RAVANA'S VIRTUOUS BROTHER, VIBHEESHANA, INTERVENED.

O KING, AN ENVOY CANNOT BE PUT TO DEATH. SPARE HIS LIFE!

ALL RIGHT. THE MONKEY SHALL LIVE, BUT HE SHALL BE MUTILATED. SET HIS TAIL ON FIRE AND TAKE HIM AROUND LANKA!

SO, OIL-SOAKED PIECES OF CLOTH WERE TIED AROUND HANUMAN'S TAIL. THEN IT WAS SET ON FIRE.

HE WAS LED THROUGH THE STREETS OF LANKA...

...BUT WHEN THE PROCESSION REACHED THE CITY GATES, HE LEAPT UP TO THE TOP.

THERE, ASSUMING A DIMINUTIVE FORM, HE CAST OFF THE ROPES THAT BOUND HIM AND BECAME FREE!

HE RESUMED HIS LARGE SIZE AND LEAPING FROM ROOF TO ROOF, HE SET FIRE TO LANKA.

HANUMAN THEN FLEW BACK TO REJOIN THE MONKEYS WAITING ON THE OTHER SIDE OF THE OCEAN.

MEANWHILE, AT KISHKINDHA, RAMA WAS WORRIED.

THE MONKEYS HAVE COMBED NORTH, EAST AND WEST. WILL THOSE WHO WENT SOUTH ALSO RETURN WITHOUT ANY NEWS?

LOOK! THERE'S A MONKEY RUNNING TOWARDS US. IT COULD BE THAT HE HAS NEWS OF SITA!

IT WAS DADHIMUKHA. HE SALUTED SUGREEVA.

MY LORD, MADHUVANA, THE GARDEN OF WHICH I AM PROTECTOR, HAS BEEN RUINED BY ANGADA AND HANUMAN AND THEIR FOLLOWERS.

EVERY TREE IN THE GARDEN HAS BEEN PLUNDERED OF ITS FRUITS!

HANUMAN HAS FOUND SITA! SO HE MUST HAVE ALLOWED THE MONKEYS TO CELEBRATE BY FEASTING ON FRUITS AND HONEY!

LET MY VICTORIOUS MONKEYS ENJOY THEMSELVES, DADHIMUKHA! THEY HAVE EARNED THESE SPOILS. BUT ASK HANUMAN TO COME HERE.

SOON —

AH! HERE HE COMES!

HANUMAN SALUTED THEM AND THEN UTTERED THE WORDS THAT FELL ON RAMA'S EARS LIKE IMMORTAL MUSIC.

LORD, I HAVE FOUND SITA. SHE IS A CAPTIVE IN LANKA, ACROSS THE SOUTHERN OCEAN. HERE IS THE JEWEL SHE ASKED ME TO GIVE YOU.

RAMA GAZED AT THE JEWEL AS IF IN A TRANCE. THEN HE TURNED TO LAKSHMANA.

WHAT COULD BE MORE PAINFUL THAN TO BEHOLD THIS JEWEL WITHOUT SITA?

HANUMAN DESCRIBED THE SITUATION IN WHICH SITA WAS PLACED.

SHE WOULD NOT LET ME CARRY HER AWAY. FOR SHE FEELS HER HONOUR WILL BE VINDICATED ONLY IF YOU COME AND VANQUISH RAVANA.

I WILL GO TO LANKA AT ONCE.

RAMA AND LAKSHMANA, ACCOMPANIED BY SUGREEVA, HANUMAN AND THE MONKEY ARMY, STARTED OUT ON THE LONG JOURNEY TO LANKA.

AT LAST THEY REACHED THE SOUTHERN SHORE.

WE WILL CAMP HERE. O VALIANT MONKEYS, WE MUST NOW FIND A WAY TO CROSS THIS GREAT OCEAN!

A LITTLE LATER —

LOOK! RAKSHASAS! BE PREPARED TO FACE AN ATTACK!

BUT THE RAKSHASAS HAD NOT COME TO ATTACK THEM —

I AM VIBHEESHANA, RAVANA'S YOUNGER BROTHER. I URGED MY BROTHER TO RESTORE SITA TO RAMA. HE REFUSED. THEREFORE, I'VE COME HERE TO JOIN RAMA. TAKE ME TO HIM.

SUGREEVA INFORMED RAMA OF VIBHEESHANA'S ARRIVAL.

RAMA, I SUSPECT A CONSPIRACY. DON'T TRUST RAVANA'S BROTHER. KILL HIM!

NO, SUGREEVA. ANYONE WHO COMES HERE SEEKING REFUGE, SHALL RECEIVE IT—

RAMA WELCOMED RAVANA'S BROTHER. AFTER A LONG DISCUSSION WITH VIBHEESHANA, RAMA WAS ABLE TO ACQUAINT HIMSELF WITH THE MILITARY STRENGTH OF THE ENEMY.

RAVANA SEEMS TO BE WELL ARMED. BUT, VIBHEE-SHANA, I WILL SURELY SLAY RAVANA!

THEN RAMA, ON VIBHEESHANA'S ADVICE, PRAYED TO SAGARA, LORD OF THE OCEAN.

O SAGARA, MAKE A PATH FOR MY ARMY TO CROSS OVER TO LANKA!

RAMA PRAYED AND FASTED FOR THREE DAYS BUT SAGARA DID NOT RESPOND. ENRAGED, RAMA TOOK AIM AT THE OCEAN.

MY PATIENCE HAS BEEN MISTAKEN FOR WEAKNESS! I SHALL DRY UP YOUR DOMAIN, O SAGARA, AND THE MONKEYS SHALL CROSS TO THE OTHER SHORE ON FOOT!

IMMEDIATELY SAGARA ROSE FROM THE OCEAN.

O RAMA, YOU HAVE WITH YOU THE MONKEY, NALA, WHO IS A GREAT BUILDER. LET HIM CON-STRUCT A BRIDGE OVER MY WATERS AND I WILL HOLD IT UP.

AT RAMA'S COMMAND, THE MONKEYS FELLED MANY TREES AND...

...CARRIED THEM TO THE SHORE.

UNDER THE SUPERVISION OF NALA, THEY BUILT A MIGHTY BRIDGE.

RAMA AND HIS PARTY CROSSED THE OCEAN.

MEANWHILE, IN LANKA, RAVANA WAS STILL TRYING TO PERSUADE SITA TO MARRY HIM.

SITA, IN A SURPRISE ATTACK LAST NIGHT, MY ARMY DESTROYED THE MONKEYS. MY COMMANDER SEVERED THE HEADS OF THE SLEEPING RAMA AND LAKSHMANA. LOOK! HERE IS RAMA'S HEAD!

OH! RAMA! RAMA!

O RAVANA, KILL ME AS WELL SO THAT I MAY FOLLOW MY HUSBAND!

AFTER RAVANA LEFT, A RAKSHASI APPROACHED SITA —

DON'T BE DECEIVED BY RAVANA. HE HAS ONLY CONJURED UP RAMA'S HEAD. RAMA IS ACTUALLY CAMPING OUTSIDE LANKA.

YOU ARE SO VERY KIND, SARAMA.

MEANWHILE, AT THE MEETING OF RAVANA'S COUNCIL —

A MONARCH SHOULD BE ON FRIENDLY TERMS, WITH HIS EQUALS, OR WITH THOSE WHO ARE STRONGER THAN HIM-SELF. RETURN SITA TO RAMA AND SEEK TO MAKE HIM AN ALLY.

WHAT? RAMA, MY EQUAL? THAT PUNY MAN WITH ONLY MONKEYS TO FIGHT FOR HIM? RAMA MAY HAVE MANAGED TO CROSS THE SEA AND REACH LANKA BUT HE WILL NOT RETURN ALIVE!

HAVING IMPROVED THE DEFENCES OF LANKA, RAVANA CLIMBED TO THE RAMPARTS TO SURVEY RAMA'S ARMY, WHICH HAD ASSEMBLED ON MOUNT SUVELA.

LOOK, THERE'S RAVANA!

ON A SUDDEN IMPULSE, SUGREEVA LEAPED FROM THE SUMMIT OF MOUNT SUVELA.

HE DESCENDED . . .

...AND FLUNG AWAY HIS DIADEM.

AFTER A BRIEF COMBAT WITH RAVANA, SUGREEVA REJOINED RAMA.

WELL DONE!

LATER, RAMA SENT PRINCE ANGADA TO RAVANA'S COURT —

IT IS NOT TOO LATE TO SAVE YOURSELF. RETURN SITA TO RAMA AND APOLOGISE, OR RAMA WILL SURELY SLAY YOU.

IMPUDENT MONKEY! SEIZE HIM! KILL HIM!

BUT ANGADA ESCAPED EFFORTLESSLY...

...AND THE BATTLE BEGAN.

THE MONKEYS LEAPT UP TO THE BATTLEMENTS...

...DRAGGED THE DEFENDING RAKSHASAS DOWN...

...AND ENGAGED THEM IN A FIERCE BATTLE THE WHOLE DAY LONG.

AS THE SUN SET, THE RAKSHASAS FOUGHT WITH RENEWED VIGOUR. RAMA AND LAKSHMANA STRUCK DOWN THE ADVANCING ARMY LED BY INDRAJIT.

INDRAJIT MADE HIMSELF INVISIBLE AND SHOWERED ARROWS ON RAMA AND LAKSHMANA. BOTH FELL DOWN, UNCONSCIOUS.

RAMA IS DEAD!

BUT, IN A LITTLE WHILE, RAMA REGAINED CONSCIOUSNESS. SEEING HIS BROTHER WHO LAY BLEEDING AND STILL UNCONSCIOUS, HE PUT HIS HEAD LOVINGLY ON HIS LAP.

GARUDA, THE DIVINE EAGLE, VEHICLE OF VISHNU, CAME AND CARESSED LAKSHMANA WITH HIS WINGS.

AT GARUDA'S TOUCH, THE WOUNDS HEALED AND LAKSHMANA REGAINED CONSCIOUSNESS.

INDRAJIT SHOT POISONOUS SNAKES IN THE GUISE OF ARROWS AT YOU AND LAKSHMANA. BEWARE OF THE RAKSHASAS! THEY ADOPT TREACHEROUS MEANS!

GARUDA FLEW AWAY. RAMA, LAKSHMANA AND THE MONKEYS CONTINUED THEIR BATTLE AGAINST THE RAKSHASAS.

RAVANA'S POWERFUL LIEUTENANTS, DHUMRAKSHA, AND PRAHASTA, ALONG WITH MANY OTHERS, WERE SLAIN.

THEN RAVANA HIMSELF MADE HIS APPEARANCE ON THE BATTLEFIELD.

BUT RAMA, RIDING ON HANUMAN'S STRONG SHOULDERS, SHATTERED RAVANA'S CHARIOT, KILLING HIS CHARIOTEER AND HORSES.

UNDER RAMA'S RAIN OF ARROWS, RAVANA LOST HIS BOW AND HIS DIADEM WAS SHATTERED.

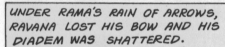

I WON'T KILL YOU, RAVANA, SINCE YOU ARE TIRED AND UN-ARMED. YOU MAY GO BACK NOW.

RAVANA SAID NOTHING. FULL OF SHAME, HE RETURNED TO HIS PALACE.

HE SUMMONED HIS COUNCILLORS.

KUMBHAKARNA IS OUR LAST HOPE! WAKE HIM UP!

THE GIANT KUMBHAKARNA WAS IN THE HABIT OF SLEEPING FOR SIX MONTHS AT A STRETCH. TO WAKE HIM UP, A GREAT DIN WAS MADE BY BEATING DRUMS, BLOWING CONCHES AND TRUMPETS.

THEY EVEN DROVE ELEPHANTS OVER HIM —

AT LAST, THE GIANT WOKE UP AND, AT THE COMMAND OF RAVANA, WENT TO THE BATTLEFIELD. THERE THE TREES AND ROCKS AIMED AT HIM BY THE MONKEYS HAD NOT THE SLIGHTEST EFFECT.

BUT, IN THE END, HE FELL, STRUCK BY ONE OF RAMA'S ARROWS.

AT A SIGN FROM SUGREEVA, THE MONKEYS ENTERED LANKA AND SET FIRE TO THE CITY.

THE RAKSHASAS GAVE WAY UNDER THE ONSLAUGHT OF THE MONKEYS, BUT AT THE DECISIVE MOMENT, INDRAJIT APPEARED —

OH, GOD! ISN'T THAT SITA?

ONE STEP FORWARD, AND I WILL KILL SITA RIGHT HERE — IN FRONT OF YOUR EYES! SHE IS THE CAUSE OF THIS WAR.

AS INDRAJIT STRUCK THE ILLUSORY SITA THE STUNNED MONKEYS STEPPED BACK AND THEN FLED.

NOW WE WILL HAVE SOME RESPITE. BEFORE THE MONKEYS RETURN TO ATTACK, I'LL PERFORM A SACRIFICE AND BECOME INVINCIBLE.

THE MONKEYS BROUGHT RAMA THE NEWS AND HE SWOONED. WHEN HE CAME TO, VIBHEESHANA CONSOLED HIM.

RAMA, PLEASE LISTEN TO ME. IT CAN'T HAVE BEEN THE REAL SITA; I KNOW THE SIGNS. FROM THE DESCRIPTION, I AM CERTAIN IT WAS ONLY ONE OF INDRAJIT'S MAGICAL CREATIONS!

THIS WILL CERTAINLY BE FOLLOWED BY A SACRIFICE WHICH WILL MAKE HIM INVINCIBLE. KILL HIM BEFORE HE COMPLETES IT!

LAKSHMANA WILL DO IT.

DISTURBED IN HIS RITES BY THE ARRIVAL OF LAKSHMANA, INDRAJIT ROSE TO THE NEW CHALLENGE.

BUT HE WAS QUICKLY FELLED BY LAKSHMANA'S SWIFT ARROW.

HIS AGONISED CRIES BROUGHT RAVANA TO THE SPOT.

TRAITOR! YOU WILL DIE NOW, VIBHEESHANA!

RAVANA TOOK DEADLY AIM AT VIBHEESHANA.

BUT, IN THE NICK OF TIME, HIS ARROW WAS BROKEN INTO TWO BY ONE OF LAKSHMANA'S ARROWS.

ENRAGED, RAVANA AIMED AGAIN AND HIS ARROW STRUCK LAKSHMANA IN THE HEART.

VALIANT MONKEYS, TAKE CARE OF MY BROTHER, LAKSHMANA, WHILE I DEAL WITH THIS MONSTROUS CREATURE. ONE OF US MUST NOW CEASE TO EXIST.

BUT AS RAMA'S ARROWS RAINED ON HIM, RAVANA FLED.

DURING THE LULL THAT FOLLOWED, RAMA KNELT, GRIEF-STRICKEN, BY HIS BROTHER'S SIDE.

LAKSHMANA, WHY DON'T YOU RISE? OPEN YOUR EYES, MY BROTHER!

A VOICE BY HIS SIDE GAVE HIM HOPE. IT WAS SUSHENA'S. THE WISE MONKEY CONSOLED RAMA.

LAKSHMANA IS IN A SWOON, THAT'S ALL. TO REVIVE HIM, WE NEED THE MEDICINAL HERBS FROM DISTANT MOUNT MAHODAYA.

MY DESPAIR HAS TURNED TO JOY! GO, DEAR HANUMAN, AND HURRY BACK WITH THE LIFE-GIVING HERB!

HANUMAN FLEW TO MAHODAYA, NEAR THE HIMALAYAS.

WHICH ARE THE HERBS? THESE OR THOSE?

OH, DEAR, I CAN'T DECIDE! I'LL CARRY THE WHOLE MOUNTAIN TO SUSHENA. HE CAN THEN SELECT THE HERB HE WANTS!

SO HANUMAN CARRIED THE MOUNTAIN ACROSS THE ENTIRE SUBCONTINENT, TO LANKA.

AT LANKA —

OH, LOOK! HANUMAN HAS BROUGHT THE WHOLE MOUNTAIN!

HANUMAN NEVER FAILS US!

UNPERTURBED, SUSHENA FOUND THE RIGHT HERB AND, CRUSHING IT, HE HELD IT TO LAKSHMANA'S NOSE.

IMMEDIATELY LAKSHMANA REGAINED CONSCIOUSNESS.

THANK GOD YOU ARE ALL RIGHT, LAKSHMANA!

HANUMAN TOOK THE MOUNTAIN BACK TO ITS ORIGINAL PLACE AND RETURNED TO RAMA.

JUST THEN A WAR CRY RENT THE AIR. RAVANA HAD ARRIVED!

RAMA MOUNTED THE CHARIOT SENT TO HIM BY INDRA, LORD OF THE DEVAS.

YOU CARRIED SITA AWAY LIKE A THIEF WHEN SHE WAS ALONE AND DEFENCELESS. YOU KNEW, IF I HAD BEEN PRESENT, I WOULD HAVE DESPATCHED YOU STRAIGHT AWAY TO JOIN KHARA!

A TERRIBLE COMBAT BETWEEN RAMA AND RAVANA FOLLOWED.

FOR A WHILE, NOTHING WAS HEARD BUT THE MIGHTY CLASH OF STEEL AGAINST STEEL. DARKNESS SEEMED TO ENVELOPE THEM AND ONLY THE SPARKS OF CLASHING STEEL WERE VISIBLE.

FINALLY, RAMA UTTERED A PRAYER * TO SURYA AND, INVOKING THE BRAHMA ASTRA, AIMED STRAIGHT AT RAVANA...

...AND RAVANA FELL DEAD.

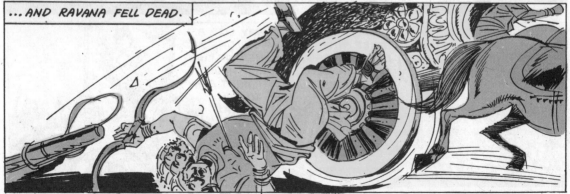

* TAUGHT BY SAGE AGASTYA ON THE BATTLEFIELD

LAKSHMANA CROWNED VIBHEESHANA THE NEW KING. PEACE AND RIGHTEOUSNESS WAS RESTORED TO LANKA.

LATER, WHEN RAMA AND SITA MET EACH OTHER ___

SITA, I'VE VINDICATED MY HONOUR. I'VE KILLED THE ABDUCTOR OF MY WIFE.

... BUT NO MAN OF HONOUR CAN TAKE BACK A WIFE WHO HAS LIVED IN THE HOUSE OF ANOTHER. WE MUST PART.

SITA WAS SHOCKED TO HEAR HIS WORDS.

IT IS A FACT THAT I WAS RAVANA'S CAPTIVE. BUT MY MIND WAS FILLED WITH ONE PERSON ALONE — RAMA! NOW THAT YOU THINK I AM IMPURE I'VE NOTHING TO LIVE FOR. LET LAKSHMANA PREPARE A PYRE. I WILL SEEK REFUGE IN AGNI *.

* THE FIRE GOD

O AGNI, IT IS NOT THAT I WANT TO PROCLAIM MY VIRTUE TO THE WORLD. BUT SINCE RAMA DEMANDS IT, SHOW THAT I AM INDEED BLAMELESS!

AGNI HEARD HER PRAYER. SHE PASSED THE TEST OF FIRE WITHOUT BURNING A SINGLE HAIR.

O RAMA, RECEIVE SITA! SHE IS PURE AND VIRTUOUS!

FORGIVE ME, SITA. I KNEW YOU WERE BLAMELESS. BUT A KING'S WIFE MUST BE ABOVE SUSPICION. THAT IS WHY THE TEST HAD TO BE UNDERGONE.

RAMA, SITA AND LAKSHMANA SET OUT FOR AYODHYA IN THE PUSHPAKA VIMANA, WHICH KING VIBHEESHANA PLACED AT THEIR DISPOSAL.

ON THE OUTSKIRTS OF AYODHYA, BHARATA WELCOMED THEM JOYFULLY.

RAMA WAS CROWNED KING OF AYODHYA.

RAMA RULED HIS KINGDOM WISELY AND STRICTLY FOLLOWED THE PATH OF DHARMA. PEOPLE FOLLOWED HIS EXAMPLE AND CARRIED OUT THEIR RESPECTIVE DUTIES. UNDER RAMA'S RULE, THERE WAS UNIVERSAL HAPPINESS.

Special Issues and
Panchatatna Series are available now.